THE EMOJI MOVIE HANDBOOK

#ALLTHE FEELS

This book belongs to:

lmelia♡

Who mostly feels:

(tick the Emoji that suits your mood best)

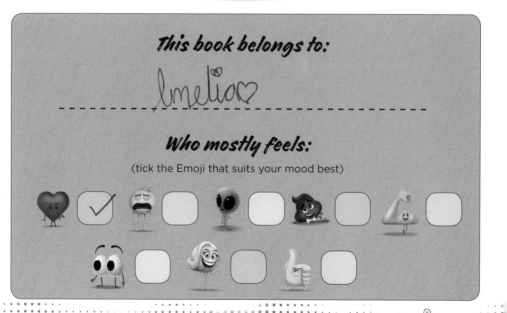

centum

Meet the Emojis!

This book is your personal guide to _The Emoji Movie._

Say hi to some of its superstars and get ready to go on the most amazing app-venture!

Hi-5
page 30

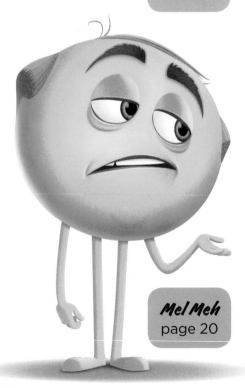

Mel Meh
page 20

Mary Meh
page 20

If you're ready for loads of cool movie facts, puzzles, games and to #EXPRESS YOURSELF then turn the page and let's go!

Textopolis

Welcome to Textopolis! The secret app-tastic world inside Alex's smartphone.

An entire civillisation of Emojis live in the text app inside Alex's phone. Each Emoji has only one expression and they happily work in the cube, sitting patiently in their squares, hoping and waiting for Alex to select them for his texts.

But there is one Emoji who is different to all the rest. Gene was born to be Meh but can express himself in all kinds of ways. He is determined to fit in though and keep this odd trait a secret. But his first day of work in the cube doesn't go exactly to plan... *#EPICFAIL!* which leads to all kinds of trouble, not just for Gene but for Alex and Textopolis too!

Continued on page 12...

@GeneMeh

The world's first fully-expressive face Emoji, Gene Meh has got the lot! Tears, laughter, anger, shame! He just needs to realise that expressing himself doesn't have to be a problem, it could be the solution!

Right from the start it is obvious Gene is special. Unlike most Mehs he can pull all kinds of faces and feel all kinds of emotions.

Emoji file

Full name: Gene Meh
Best at: being emotional
Not so good at: keeping a Meh face
Life goal: to be Meh
Most likely to: doubt himself

GENE'S EXPRESSIONS

Technology is really amazing!

Gene thinks his folks are ashamed of him, but he doesn't want to hide away. He's an Emoji, he's just not sure which one!

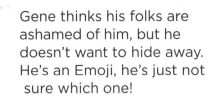

Working in the cube is an Emoji's whole purpose in life!

Cool colour

Use the picture opposite to add the right colours to Gene and his best buds Hi-5 and Jailbreak.

... continued from page 7

The cube

Gene's dream of working in the cube soon turns into a horrible nightmare!

Every Emoji wants to be chosen by Alex for his texts and Gene cannot believe it when he is selected on his first day at the cube.
His folks Mary and Mel Meh are worried for him, hoping he doesn't mess up. Gene hypes himself up as his Emoji Meh face is selected, but then his face freezes, then changes into a million different emotions and not one is Meh! Arghhhhhhh! *#MALFUNCTION!*

Gene is horrified. His folks, Mary and Mel, are totes shocked. Smiler, who is in charge of the text app, is stunned! Gene's malfunction has put all of the other Emojis in danger. If Emojis can't be counted on to express just one emotion, what will happen to Textopolis?

I really went kind of Emo-explosive in there!

Smiler may be smiling but she is determined to put an end to Gene's malfunctioning Meh ways and sentences him to be deleted by the AV Bots. *#HOLYDELETO* Gene is terrified. He only wants to be normal like the other Emojis and wishes he could be just Meh and not who he really is. Ashamed and frightened he runs away.

Continued on page 24...

Odd Emoji out

Can you spot the odd Emoji out in each row?

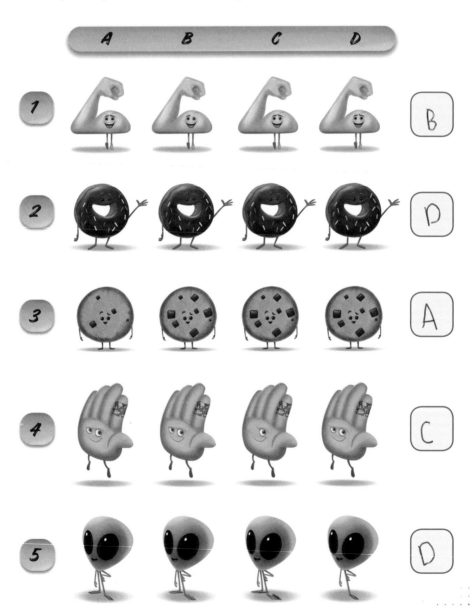

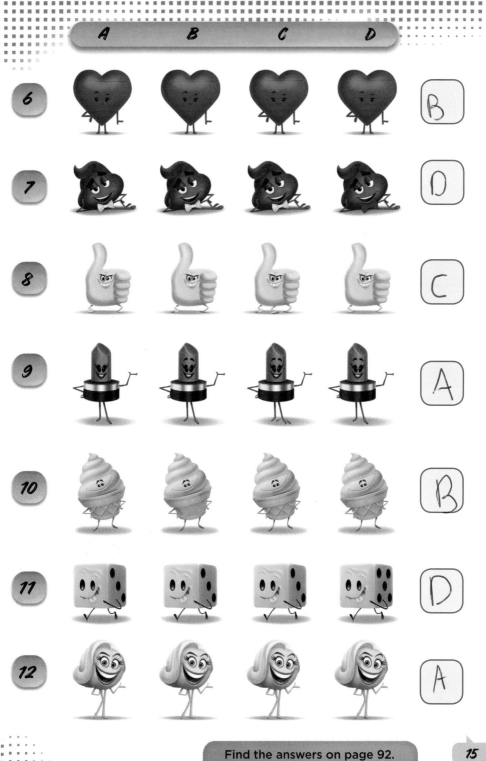

Find the answers on page 92.

Emoji escape!

Gene needs you! Help him escape his folks, Smiler and the AV Bots by working out where they are in Textopolis and marking them with an X and their name on the map.

Find Mel!
Go north 3 squares.
Head east 4 squares.
Drop south 2 squares.

Spot Mary!
Head east
4 squares.
Go north 3 squares.
Turn west 2 squares.

Will these clues
help **reveal Smiler?**
Head east 3 squares.
Go north 5 squares.
Turn west 2 squares.

Track this bot.
Head north 6 squares.
Turn east 3 squares.
Go south 1 square.

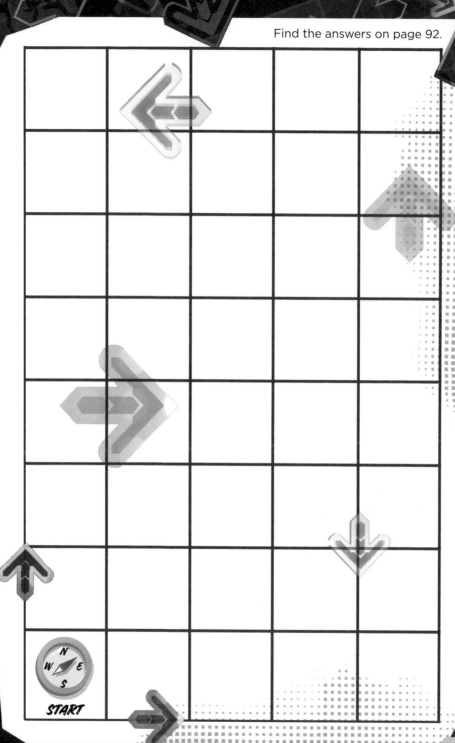

Find the answers on page 92.

Express yourself

Fill in the page with all the brilliant things that make you uniquely you... and nobody else!

name: _Amelia_

nickname: _MeMe_

birthday: _7-04.18_

age: _9_

year born: _2009_

star sign: _Amelia_

home town/city: _Brighton_

Snapchat/IG handle:

Being a princess stinks!

#SHHHHhhhhhhh!
Not many people know that I:

How I feel when...   I wake up   am at school   am with my pals

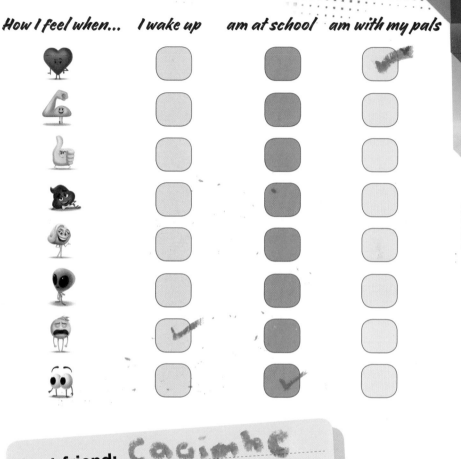

best friend: Caoimhe

pets: dog

biggest achievement: 2 Place in Swimming

proudest moment:

most embarrassing moment:

best thing about me:

eMel & eMary

Mel and Mary Meh are Gene's long-suffering parents. They may look like normal Mehs, but Mel is hiding a secret from his son and his wife which threatens to rip his family apart!

Emoji file

Full name: Mel Meh
Best at: hiding his emotions
Not so good at: expressing himself
Life goal: to hide his secret
Most likely to: do a good job of looking Meh all of the time

Emoji file

Full name: Mary Meh
Best at: looking like she doesn't care
Not so good at: expressing herself
Life goal: to protect her son
Most likely to: look totally Meh

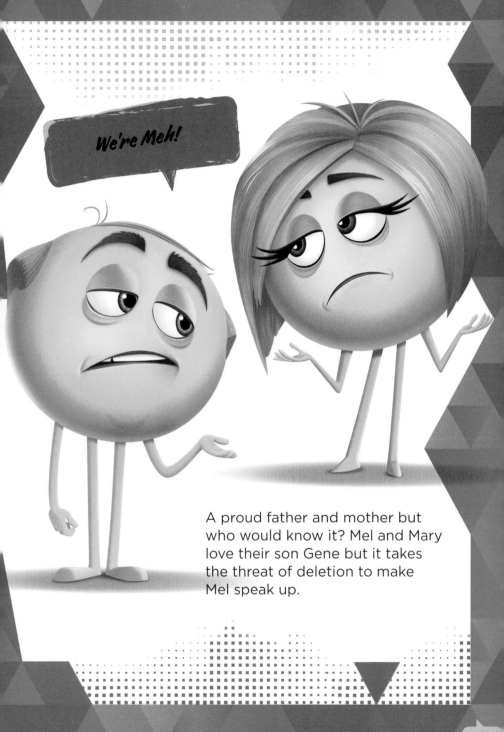

A proud father and mother but who would know it? Mel and Mary love their son Gene but it takes the threat of deletion to make Mel speak up.

... continued from page 13

Fast friends

Gene races away from Smiler and her army of deleting AV Bots, wishing he could find a way to become normal or, failing that, hide forever.

Luckily for Gene, help is at hand. Literally at hand, in the handy shape of Hi-5. Equally disillusioned with life and sad about his lack of fame and status in the cube, Hi-5 is on his own quest to become a favourite again and return to the favourites section of the cube.

I'm not going to be Meh, I'm going to be me.

I was a favourite once!

Promising Gene he knows Textopolis like, well like the back of his hand, Hi-5 convinces Gene that they should escape to the Cloud together, where they'll be safe. Or possibly find some amazing coder who can reprogram Gene to be a normal Meh and help Hi-5 to become a favourite again.

I plan to be celebrating in the favourites section by dinner.

Continued on page 36...

Express yourself

Fill in the page with all your fave things.

FAVE...

friend: ....

family member: ....

movie: ....

tv show: ....

vlogger: ....

chocolate bar: ....

song: ....

shop: ....

animal: ....

sport: ....

food: ....

drink: ....

time of year: ....

day of the week: ....

26

How I feel when...	I eat	I play sport	I hear music
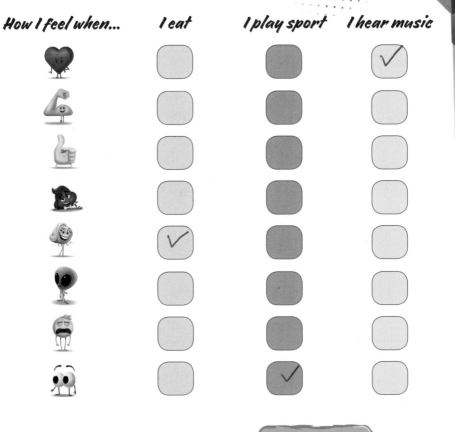	☐	☐	✓
	☐	☐	☐
	☐	☐	☐
	☐	☐	☐
	✓	☐	☐
	☐	☐	☐
	☐	☐	☐
	☐	✓	☐

#TLF

The thing I love most in the world is:

Family
Frinds
Cotten candy

Spot it!

Can you find 10 differences between these pictures of Gene and Hi-5?

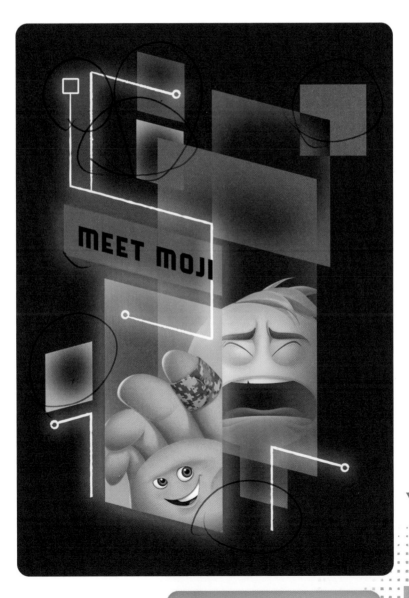

MEET MOJI

Find the answers on page 92.

@Hi-5!

Regaining his fame is the name of the game for this once-popular Emoji, until he runs into Gene and makes his first real friend.

Hi-5 is always trying to sneak back into the favourites hall, but none of the other popular Emojis will share their squares with him. When Gene smashes into him, shouting about the attacking AV Bots, Hi-5 thinks they're after him.

Emoji file

Full name: Hi-5
Best at: being the centre of attention
Not so good at: being ignored
Life goal: to be famous again
Most likely to: show you some skin

Hi-5 proves himself a useful right-hand man to his buddy Gene when it comes to escaping the AV Bots, thanks to his knowledge of Alex's smartphone.

Don't worry I got game. Mad game!

This handy Emoji proves he's got the moves in the dance app, including an **#AWESOME** moonwalk. He boogies on down to reach the next level and help his pals escape the app.

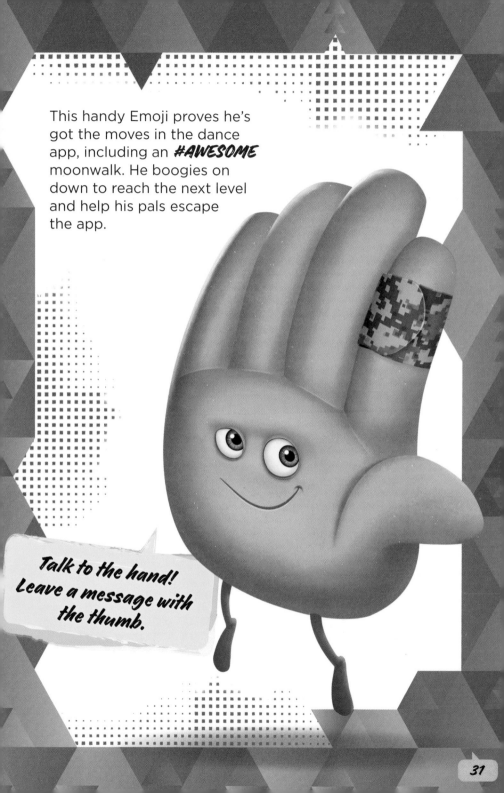

Talk to the hand! Leave a message with the thumb.

Doodletastic

Grab your pencil and get creative with your Emoji doodles.

Carry on this Emoji pattern to fill the square.

Think happy thoughts and turn these squiggles into some positive Emojis!

Doodle a double for Gene in 3 simple steps!

1. Draw a circle and add some hair.

2. Doodle in some half-circle eyes and a Meh smile.

3. Add two wiggly eyebrows and colour him in.

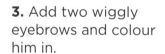

Draw your Gene here.

Timewarp

Check out all these fun facts about smartphones and Emojis.

World War I pioneered many technological innovations. Field telephones and wireless communications were regularly used for the first time to communicate military movements between 1914 and 1919.

In 1983, Motorola released its first commercial mobile phone, known as the Motorola DynaTAC 8000X. The handset offered 30 minutes of talk time, and could store 30 phone numbers. It cost more than £2,000.

The world's first mobile phone call was made on 3 April 1973, when Martin Cooper, an engineer at Motorola, called a rival telecoms company and informed them he was speaking via a mobile phone. The phone weighed a whopping 1.1kg and was around 22cm long. With this prototype device, you got about 30 minutes of talk time and it took around 10 hours to charge.

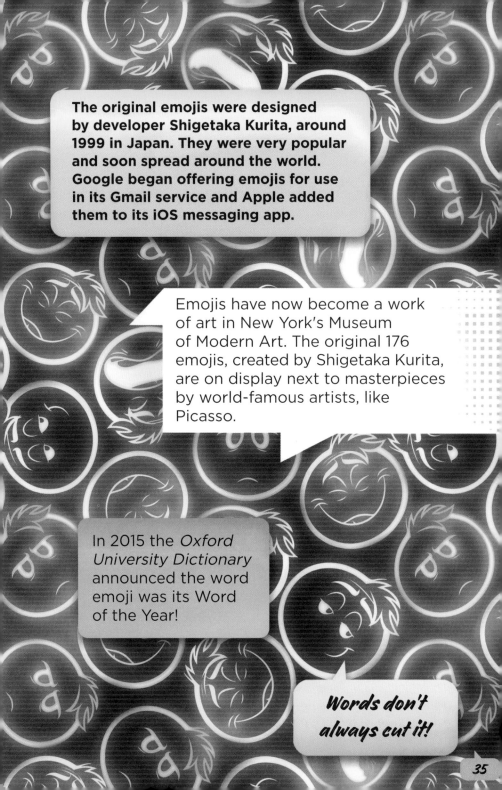

The original emojis were designed by developer Shigetaka Kurita, around 1999 in Japan. They were very popular and soon spread around the world. Google began offering emojis for use in its Gmail service and Apple added them to its iOS messaging app.

Emojis have now become a work of art in New York's Museum of Modern Art. The original 176 emojis, created by Shigetaka Kurita, are on display next to masterpieces by world-famous artists, like Picasso.

In 2015 the *Oxford University Dictionary* announced the word emoji was its Word of the Year!

Words don't always cut it!

... continued from page 25

Pixel princess

Hi-5 and Gene continue their app-venture to find the Cloud but soon realise that to get there they'll need to break through the Firewall!

Luckily for them they meet the smart and sassy Jailbreak, who has the coding skills to break through the Firewall. Unluckily for them she's not interested in helping them. Jailbreak only looks out for No 1.

This conversation is a challenge!

But Jailbreak can't help but be intrigued by Gene's ability to change his face and emotions so easily. He's like magic! She wonders if Gene could be the key to getting past the Firewall. Perhaps he could help her leave all the other rebel pirates behind and escape to the Cloud herself.

Gotta look out for number one!

For Jailbreak has her own secret. She is really a princess who hides her shiny crown under her beanie hat and instead of smiling and looking pretty spends her time coding and rebelling against the system. She is amazed to discover that Gene is just like her, and she's not the only one who feels all wrong. She agrees to help him but is determined to keep her own secret identity hidden.

Continued on page 62...

Colour copy

Colour in the Hi-5 below with your left hand and the Hi-5 opposite with your right hand. Which one looks better?

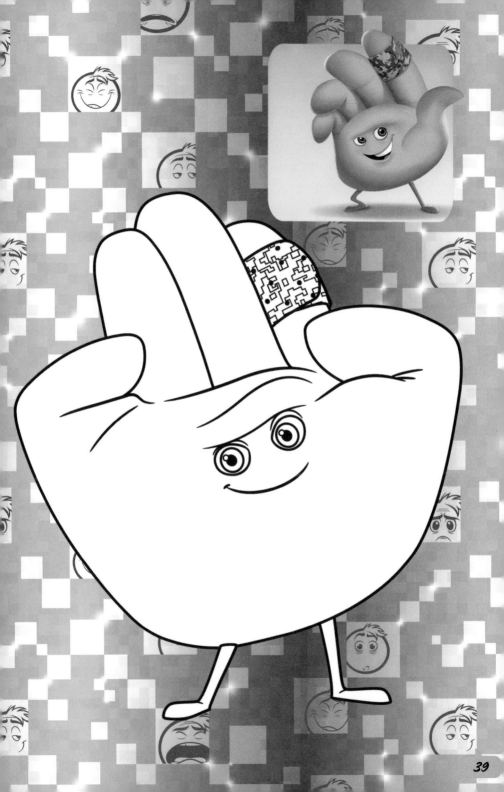

Express yourself

Fill in the page with all your thoughts and feelings about your family!

Who in your family is...

happiest: ....

messiest: ....

loudest: ....

kindest: ....

chattiest: ....

funniest: ....

cuddliest: ....

How I feel about...   *family meals*   *family holidays*

	family meals	family holidays
♥	☐	☐
👍	☐	☐
😓	☐	☐

Doodle it here. ↘

#FAMILYSELFIE

If your folks were an Emoji what would they look like?

#FAMILYLOVE

The best thing about my family is:

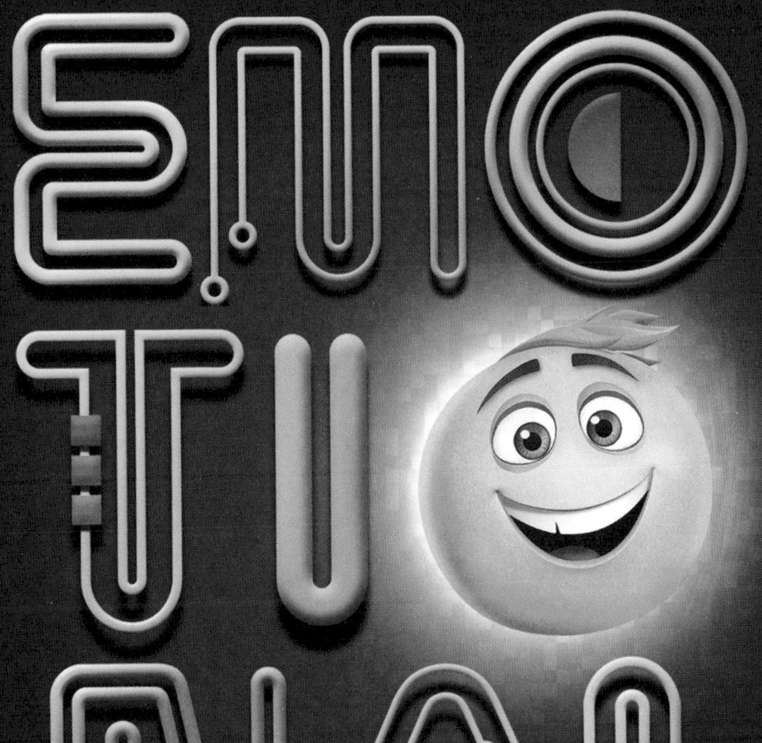
EMOTIONAL

Text talk

Ever struggle to type your texts quick enough or understand your mates' messages? Read on for some app-tastic abbreviations.

2DAY: Today
4EAE: For ever and ever
ADN: Any day now
AFK: Away from keyboard
ATM: At the moment
B4: Before
BF / GF: Boyfriend / Girlfriend
BFN: Bye for now
BOL: Be on later
BRB: Be right back
BTW: By the way
CUL: See you later
DM: Direct message
DWBH: Don't worry, be happy
F2F or FTF: Face to face
FWIW: For what it's worth

FYEO: For your eyes only
FYI: For your information
GR8: Great
HAK: Hugs and kisses
HAND: Have a nice day
HTH: Hope this helps / Happy to help
IDK: I don't know
IIRC: If I remember correctly
IKR: I know, right?
ILY / ILU: I love you
IMHO: In my honest opinion / In my humble opinion
IMO: In my opinion
IRL: In real life
IU2U: It's up to you
IYKWIM: If you know what I mean
J/K: Just kidding
JSYK: Just so you know
K or KK: Okay

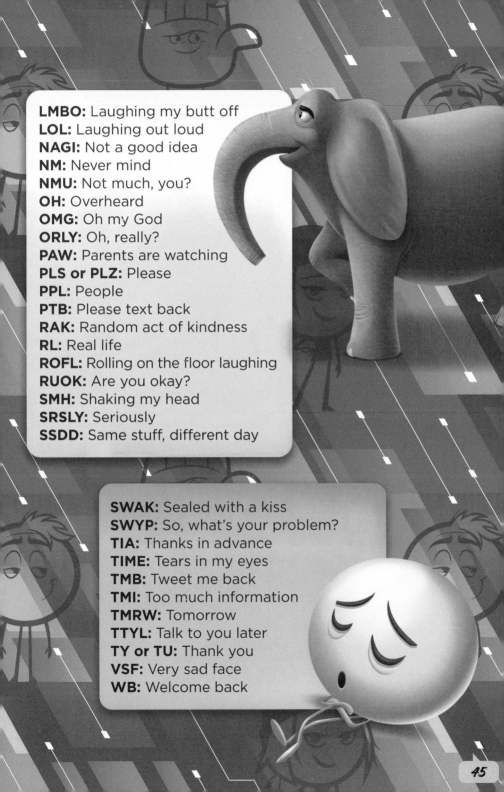

LMBO: Laughing my butt off
LOL: Laughing out loud
NAGI: Not a good idea
NM: Never mind
NMU: Not much, you?
OH: Overheard
OMG: Oh my God
ORLY: Oh, really?
PAW: Parents are watching
PLS or PLZ: Please
PPL: People
PTB: Please text back
RAK: Random act of kindness
RL: Real life
ROFL: Rolling on the floor laughing
RUOK: Are you okay?
SMH: Shaking my head
SRSLY: Seriously
SSDD: Same stuff, different day

SWAK: Sealed with a kiss
SWYP: So, what's your problem?
TIA: Thanks in advance
TIME: Tears in my eyes
TMB: Tweet me back
TMI: Too much information
TMRW: Tomorrow
TTYL: Talk to you later
TY or TU: Thank you
VSF: Very sad face
WB: Welcome back

Dance off

Find a friend and see how who can help Gene, Hi-5 and Jailbreak shake thier stuff across the dance floor with this fun game. Follow the rules opposite and the first one to reach Level 2 wins.

DANCE

9

8

Wow! Cool moves, have another go.

1

Start

7

2

6

3

Ooops, you messed up a dance step, miss a go.

4

5

What you need:
- a coin for each player
- a die

How to play:
1. Take it in turns to roll the die and move across the board.
2. Every time you land on a move forward 3 spaces.
3. When you land a  go back 3 spaces.
4. First player to Level 2 wins.

| | | **22**  | **23** *Oh no! You tripped instead of twirled. Miss a go.* |

| **10** | **21** | | |

| **11** | **20** | | **24** |

| **12** | **19** | **18** *Shake those shoulders and have another go.* | **25**  *You made it to Level 2! You're a winner!* |

| **13**  *Point your disco finger and boogie forward 2 spaces.* | | **17**  |  **LET'S SHAKE IT!** |

| **14** | **15** | **16** | |

Trash terror!

Oh no! Hi-5 has landed in the Trash. Which path should Gene take to find and rescue him?

Which path will lead Gene to the pixel pirate?

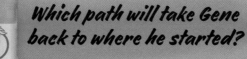

Which path will take Gene back to where he started?

PIXEL
PIRATE

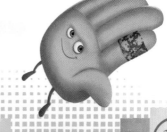

@Jailbreak

This rebel princess transforms into a pixel pirate to get what she wants.

Nifty coding skills and an ability to make the most of an opportunity help Jailbreak hook up with Gene and achieve her dream of breaking through the Firewall.

I knew there was more to life!

Emoji file

Full name: Jailbreak (aka Princess)
Best at: keeping a secret
Not so good at: playing by the rules
Life goal: to cross the Firewall and reach the Cloud
Most likely to: look out for number one

Gene and Hi-5 discover Jailbreak in the Dictionary app, which is really a skin pirate app, and hope she will use her clever coding skills to reprogram Gene to be a normal Meh and help Hi-5 to become a favourite again.

Get to the Cloud and you can be anyone you want to be.

She may have some cool coding moves but Jailbreak's dancing is decidedly off-beat, until Gene shows her how to let her emotions guide her motions!

Quick colour

How quickly can you colour in all these Emojis? Ready, steady, GO!

Express yourself

**Fill in the page with all
your dreams...**

My dream...

job:

holiday:

outfit:

day:

meal:

What do you dream about most?

 love ☐

 school ☐

 celebs ☐

 family ☐

 aliens ☐

 ghosts ☐

 food ☐

 movies ☐

DREAM DECODER

Dream big and the sky is the limit, but what do your sleep dreams really mean?

Flying dreams – if you dream you are flying high it usually means you feel confident.

Falling dreams - if you dream you falling out of the sky or down a hole, or just tripping up and falling over it can mean you're feeling out of control.

Being naked dreams - Yikes! This usually means you're feeling a bit worried about something, or that you're trying to hide something.

Emoji count-up

How many of the Emojis below can you count on the page?

Find the answers on page 92.

@Smiler

She's sneaky, she's mean, she's menacing but she's always smiling!

Fluttering eyelashes, hot pink liptstick and a killer smile are the perfect mask for this sneaky Emoji, who is out to destroy Gene and anything that threatens her beloved Textopolis.

SMILE LIKE YOU MEAN IT

Emoji file

Full name: Smiler
Best at: flashing her teeth
Not so good at: being genuine
Life goal: to always be cheerful
Least likely to: look how she feels

When you smile you can pretty much say anything you want.

Being the original Emoji means Smiler is the *#BOSS* of the cube.

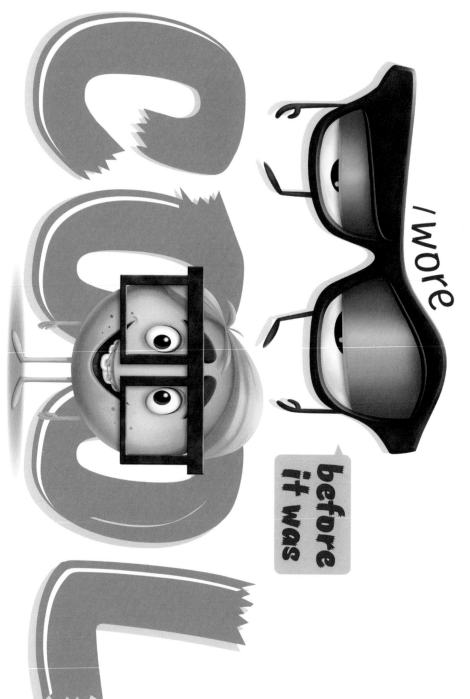

... continued from page 37

App-ventures

Jailbreak, Gene and Hi-5 continue on their journey through the smartphone apps with hilarious but dangerous results, both for them and Alex.

Alex is busy minding his own business at school when his phone really starts to play up! One minute it's blaring out music when he should be quiet in class, the next beeping and buzzing when he's trying to talk to his secret crush Addie. *#CRINGE!*

He has no idea it's because Gene, Jailbreak and Hi-5 are storming their way through a series of apps, trying to find their way to the Firewall and avoid the dreaded AV Bots from deleting Gene forever.

But as Gene helps Jailbreak boogie her way through some complicated dance steps and Hi-5 discover what friendship is all about, he grows closer to his new pals.

Sorry. Friends don't let friends play game apps!

Let your emotions guide your motions.

As the Emojis open up to each other, Gene is surprised that his two buddies don't see him as a malfunctioning oddball but as the brave, funny and charming soul he is on the inside. For the first time in his life, Gene feels like he can express himself!

Continued on page 72...

Sweet stuff

Help Gene, Jailbreak and Hi-5 escape from the game app by following the sweets in the order opposite through the maze.

Start

I need my candy fix!

Finish

Find the answers on page 92.

Express yourself

Fill in the page with all your thoughts and feelings about your school and hobbies!

English ☐
Maths ☐
Science ☐
Geography ☐
PE ☐
History ☐
Art ☐
Music ☐

Number these subjects 1 to 8 in order of preference. 1 is your fave!

My best school subject is:

_____

_____

My main talents are:

1. _____

2. _____

3. _____

What do you like to get up to in your freetime and how do you feel about each of these hobbies and activities?

	❤️	👍	😟
reading			
football			
swimming			
takeaways			
playing music			
listening to music			
singing			
playing games			
watching tv			
watching movies			

#MUNCHTIME

When I have a spare moment I love to:

Meh face off

Grab your yellow pen and add some colour to the many expressive faces of this very special Meh!

Emoji who's who!

Do you know your Poop Daddy from your Poop Jnr? Read on to make sure you're always using the right Emoji!

Poop Daddy	Alien	Eyeballs
Ice cream	Glasses	Dice
Lips	Monkey	Moon
Thumbs Down	Cookie	Donut

Sleepy

Nerd

Slobbering

Heart

Bicep

Thumbs Up

Angry Coffee

Pizza

Lipstick

Poop Jnr

Hammer

Elephant

Bathtub

Devil

Flying Money

Shrimp

Wind

Flamenco

... continued from page 63

Happy endings

Alex is confused about what is going on with his smartphone and threatens Gene's quest for survival when he decides to take matters into his own hands.

The Emojis' app-ventures are playing havoc with Alex's smartphone and he starts deleting apps to stop the chaos. Then he makes the fateful decision to get his phone fixed once and for all.

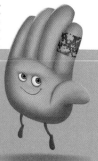

But when Alex deletes his dance app he deletes Hi-5 with it and Gene must venture into the Trash to save him.

Meanwhile Mel is expressing some secrets of his own to Mary. He tells her it is his fault Gene is like he is and 'fesses up that he too is a malfunction and can feel lots of different emotions. He shows her his different faces only to be discovered by the AV Bots who then capture him for deletion. *#HOLYDELETO*

Gene saves Hi-5 from a horrible troll in the Trash. But then the AV Bots are chasing them again, this time towards the Firewall. Gene helps Jailbreak break through to the Cloud and realises he could now be hacked to become a normal Meh.
But Gene is enjoying feeling all that he does and begs Jailbreak to return to Textopolis with him. He is heartbroken when she says no.

Gene gives himself up but discovers the entire phone is in danger due to Alex's decision to wipe them all out. Jailbreak discovers she can't give everything up to stay in the Cloud and swoops in on a giant bird to rescue Gene from the AV Bots. She tells Gene they must work together to save Alex's smartphone.

Alex is amazed to see all his Emojis waving at him from his phone and when Addie tells him she loves one of his messages, that he never had the guts to send, he realises his phone has been working to help him **#EXPRESSHIMSELF** and decides to keep it as it is. He selects Gene to show Addie how he's feeling as Gene is showing every emotion and that's exactly how Alex feels. **#SOHAPPY**

Express colour

Grab your pens and express yourself with a splash of colour!

Blast this Wind Emoji with your fave colour.

Give Poop Jnr a change and make him the same colour as your bedroom.

Look out of your window and make Lips the same colour as the sky.

Close your eyes and colour this Emoji in with the first colour you think of.

Colour in High Heel to match the clothes you're wearing right now.

Cheer Gene up and make him a bright fun colour.

So crafty

Create your own Emoji bookmark by following these simple instructions and using the template opposite.

1

Cut out the square from the opposite page and fold it in half.

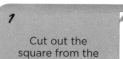

2

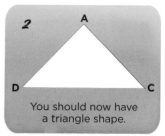

You should now have a triangle shape.

3

Fold point C up to point A.

4

Then fold point D up to point A make a diamond shape.

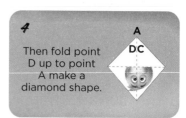

5

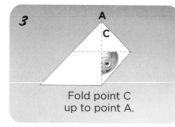

Open it back up into a triangle shape then fold one of the points A down to point B.

6

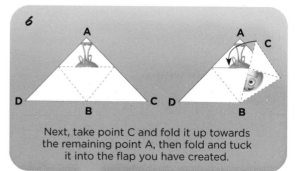

Next, take point C and fold it up towards the remaining point A, then fold and tuck it into the flap you have created.

7

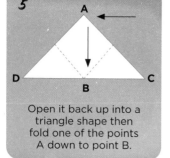

Then do the same again, this time for point D and fold and tuck it into the flap.

8

Your bookmark should then look like this.

9

Rotate it so the flap pocket is at the top, and can be slotted over the pages in your book.

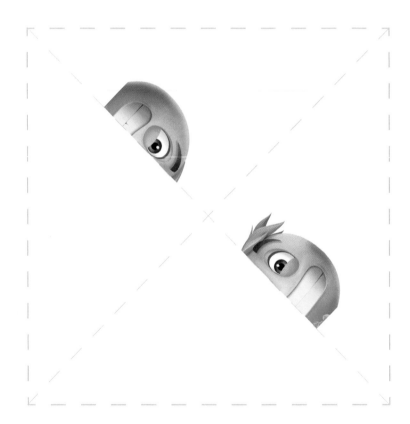

Music madness

Help Gene and his friends through the music maze.

Start

Finish

Find the answers on page 92.

All the feels

Before Emojis came along peeps had to work out how other people were feeling from what they said, how they said it and how they looked when they were saying it. Become an expert at reading body language with the clues below.

Crossed arms and legs = resistance to your ideas.

A real smile crinkles the eyes. Take note Smiler!

If someone mirrors what your body is doing and copies your body language it means that the conversation is going well.

Standing tall shows leadership and positive thoughts. Slouching = not so much!

Raised eyebrows often signal discomfort and/or distrust, alarm, surprise or fear!

A clenched jaw can signal stress or anger.

If someone avoids eye contact or tries to hold it too long, they could be telling lies, or feeling shy. In some cultures it's also a sign of respect to avoid eye contact.

Match up

Pick up a pencil and draw a line between the matching pairs of Emojis on this page.

1

2

3

4

5

6

7

8

9

10

11

12

13

14

15

16

18

19

17

21

22

20

23

24

Find the answers on page 92.

Spot it

The smaller pictures opposite may all look the same as the big picture below but something is different in each one. Can you spot what?

We're Cloudin'

Find the answers on page 92.

Express yourself

Fill in the page with all your thoughts and feelings about holidays!

summer ☐
winter ☐
adventure ☐
beach ☐
city break ☐
camping ☐
safari ☐
ski-ing ☐

Number these holiday types 1 to 8 in order of preference. 1 is best!

Best holiday memory ever:

Worst holiday memory ever:

If you could choose an Emoji to take on your next holiday, who would it be:

If you could choose a friend or family member to go on holiday with, who would it be:

_____

If you could choose a celebrity to take on your next holiday, who would it be:

#BOOKWORM

Best book you've ever read on holiday:

#SWEETBEAT

Best tune for chilling on holiday to:

#UGH #ZZZ #WAKE UP
#MONDAYS

89

Quiz time

Put your Emoji know-how to the test with this #GENIUS quiz.

1. What are Gene's parents called?
A) Mary and Mike
B) Mandy and Mel
C) Mary and Mel

2. Whose phone are the Emojis existing inside?
A) Alex's
B) Addie's
C) Smiler's

3. What kind of army does Smiler send to capture and delete Gene?
A) Zombie rodents
B) AV Bots
C) Killer pixels

4. Which area has Hi-5 sneaked into when Gene first meets him?
A) The favourites
B) The losers
C) The overs

5. What skin app is Jailbreak's piracy app hidden behind?
A) Instagram
B) Snapchat
C) Dictionary

6. What is Jailbreak's true Emoji identity?
A) Alien
B) Princess
C) Elephant

7. What does Gene need to get past to reach the Cloud?
A) Security gates
B) A brick wall
C) The Firewall

8. What kind of animal does Jailbreak swoop in on, to rescue Gene?
A) a bird
B) a bat
C) a dragon

Find the answers on page 92.

Odd Emoji out

Can you spot the odd Emoji out in each row?

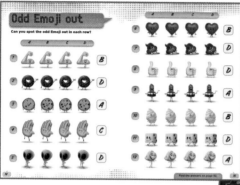

Emoji escape!

Spot it!

Can you find 10 differences between these pictures of Gene and Hi-5?

Trash terror!

Oh no! Hi-5 has landed in the Trash. Which path should Gene take to find and rescue him?

Which path will take Gene back to where he started?

Paths 3 and 4

Path 1

Which path will lead Gene to the pixel pirate?

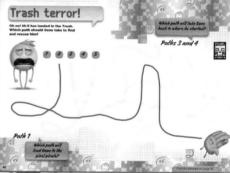

Emoji count-up

How many of the Emojis below can you count on the page?

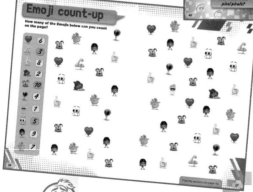

Sweet stuff

Help Gene, Jailbreak and Hi-5 escape Candy Crush by following the sweets in the order opposite through the maze.

Start

I need my candy fix!

Finish

Find the answers on page 92.

Music madness

Help Gene and his friends through the music maze.

Start

Finish

Find the answers on page 92.

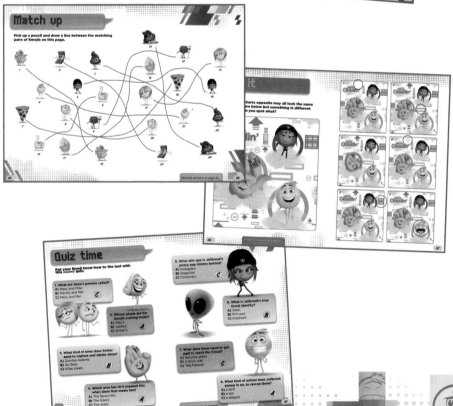

Match up

Pick up a pencil and draw a line between the matching pairs of Emojis on this page.

Find the answers on page 92.

Spot it

...tures opposite may all look the same ...re below but something is different ...n you spot what?

Quiz time

Put your Emoji know-how to the test with this **secret** quiz.

1. What are Gene's parents called?
A) Mary and Mike
B) Mandy and Mel
C) Mary and Mel
C

2. Whose phone are the Emojis existing inside?
A) Alex's
B) Addie's
C) Smiler's
A

3. What kind of army does Smiler send to capture and delete Gene?
A) Zombie rodents
B) AV Bots
C) Killer pixels
B

4. Which area has Hi-5 sneaked into when Gene first meets him?
A) The favourites
B) The losers
C) The overs
A

5. What skin app is Jailbreak's piracy app hidden behind?
A) Instagram
B) Snapchat
C) Dictionary
C

6. What is Jailbreak's true Emoji identity?
A) Alien
B) Princess
C) Elephant
B

7. What does Gene need to get past to reach the Cloud?
A) Security gates
B) A brick wall
C) The Firewall
C

8. What kind of animal does Jailbreak swoop in on, to rescue Gene?
A) A bird
B) A bat
C) A dragon
A

Find the answers on page 92.